This book belongs to:

_____

HOW I
FEEL AND
STUFF

DAILY MOOD TRACKER

Date: _____

MORNING ☀

Well   Okay   Badly

I feel... 😊 🙂 😐 🙁 😣   I slept... 🙂 😐 🙁

Today I want to... 💡   ❤ Self Care:

1. _____

2. _____

3. _____

My most important thing today is...
_____

⭐ EVENING

I feel... 😊 🙂 😐 🙁 😣   Today in a word?   Today's Energy Level

1 2 3 4 5

I'm grateful for...

1. _____

2. _____

3. _____

Today's biggest challenge was...
_____

The best part of today was...
_____

Date: _____

MORNING ☀

I feel... 😊 🙂 😐 🙁 😠   I slept... 🙂 😐 🙁
                                        Well Okay Badly

Today I want to... 💡   ♥ Self Care: _____

1. _____

2. _____

3. _____

My most important thing today is...
_____

☆ EVENING

I feel... 😊 🙂 😐 🙁 😠   Today in a word?   Today's
                                                   Energy Level
I'm grateful for...   1 2 3 4 5

1. _____

2. _____

3. _____

Today's biggest challenge was...
_____

The best part of today was...
_____

Date: _____

MORNING ☀

I feel... 😊 🙂 😐 🙁 😣   I slept... Well Okay Badly 🙂 😐 🙁

Today I want to... 💡   ♡ Self Care:

1. _____

2. _____

3. _____

My most important thing today is...
_____

⭐ EVENING

I feel... 😊 🙂 😐 🙁 😣   Today in a word?   Today's Energy Level

1 2 3 4 5

I'm grateful for...

1. _____

2. _____

3. _____

Today's biggest challenge was...
_____

The best part of today was...
_____

Date: _____

MORNING ☀

Well Okay Badly

I feel... 😌 🙂 😐 🙁 😣   I slept... 🙂 😐 🙁

Today I want to... 💡   ♥ Self Care: _____

1. _____

2. _____

3. _____

My most important thing today is...
_____

⭐ EVENING

I feel... 😌 🙂 😐 🙁 😣

I'm grateful for...

Today in a word? _____   Today's Energy Level

1 2 3 4 5

1. _____

2. _____

3. _____

Today's biggest challenge was...
_____

The best part of today was...
_____

Date: _____

MORNING ☀

I feel... 😊 🙂 😐 🙁 😣   I slept... 🙂 😐 🙁

Today I want to... 💡   ♥ Self Care:

1. _____

2. _____

3. _____

My most important thing today is...

_____

☆ EVENING

I feel... 😊 🙂 😐 🙁 😣   Today in a word?   Today's Energy Level

1 2 3 4 5

I'm grateful for...

1. _____

2. _____

3. _____

Today's biggest challenge was...

_____

The best part of today was...

_____

Date: _____

MORNING

I feel... 😊 🙂 😐 🙁 😣   I slept...   Well Okay Badly
🙂 😐 🙁

Today I want to... 💡   ♡ Self Care:

1. _____

2. _____

3. _____

My most important thing today is...

_____

⭐ EVENING

I feel... 😊 🙂 😐 🙁 😣   Today in a word?   Today's Energy Level

1 2 3 4 5

I'm grateful for...

1. _____

2. _____

3. _____

Today's biggest challenge was...

_____

The best part of today was...

_____

Date: _____

MORNING ☀

I feel... 😋 🙂 😐 🙁 😠   I slept...   Well Okay Badly
                                          😊   😐   🙁

Today I want to... 💡   ♥ Self Care: _____

1. _____

2. _____

3. _____

My most important thing today is...
_____

⭐ EVENING

I feel... 😋 🙂 😐 🙁 😠   Today in a word?   Today's Energy Level

I'm grateful for...   (   )   1 2 3 4 5

1. _____

2. _____

3. _____

Today's biggest challenge was...
_____

The best part of today was...
_____

Date: _____

MORNING ☀

I feel... 😃 🙂 😐 🙁 😣   I slept... 🙂 😐 🙁

Today I want to... 💡   ❤ Self Care:

1. _____

2. _____

3. _____

My most important thing today is...

_____

⭐ EVENING

I feel... 😃 🙂 😐 🙁 😣

Today in a word?

Today's Energy Level

1 2 3 4 5

I'm grateful for...

1. _____

2. _____

3. _____

Today's biggest challenge was...

_____

The best part of today was...

_____

Date: _____

MORNING ☼

I feel... 😋 🙂 😐 🙁 😣   I slept... 🙂 😐 🙁

Today I want to... 💡   ♥ Self Care: _____

1. _____

2. _____

3. _____

My most important thing today is...
_____

⭐ EVENING

I feel... 😋 🙂 😐 🙁 😣   Today in a word?   Today's Energy Level

I'm grateful for...   1 2 3 4 5

1. _____

2. _____

3. _____

Today's biggest challenge was...
_____

The best part of today was...
_____

Date: _____

MORNING ☀

I feel... 😊 🙂 😐 🙁 😣   I slept... 🙂 😐 🙁

Today I want to... 💡   ♥ Self Care:

1. _____

2. _____

3. _____

My most important thing today is...

☆ EVENING

I feel... 😊 🙂 😐 🙁 😣   Today in a word?   Today's Energy Level

                                                            1 2 3 4 5

I'm grateful for...

1. _____

2. _____

3. _____

Today's biggest challenge was...

The best part of today was...

Date: _____

MORNING ☀

I feel... 😕 🙂 😐 🙁 😣   I slept... 🙂 😐 🙁

Today I want to... 💡   ♥ Self Care: _____

1. _____

2. _____

3. _____

My most important thing today is...

_____

⭐ EVENING

I feel... 😕 🙂 😐 🙁 😣   Today in a word?   Today's Energy Level

1 2 3 4 5

I'm grateful for...

1. _____

2. _____

3. _____

Today's biggest challenge was...

_____

The best part of today was...

_____

Date: _____

MORNING ☀

I feel... 😋 🙂 😐 🙁 😣   I slept... 🙂 😐 🙁

Today I want to... 💡   ♡ Self Care:

1. _____

2. _____

3. _____

My most important thing today is...

_____

☆ EVENING

I feel... 😋 🙂 😐 🙁 😣   Today in a word?   Today's Energy Level

I'm grateful for...   1 2 3 4 5

1. _____

2. _____

3. _____

Today's biggest challenge was...

_____

The best part of today was...

_____

Date: _____

MORNING ☼

Well Okay Badly

I feel... 😊 🙂 😐 🙁 😠   I slept... 🙂 😐 🙁

Today I want to... 💡   ♡ Self Care: _____

1. _____

2. _____

3. _____

My most important thing today is...

_____

⭐ EVENING

I feel... 😊 🙂 😐 🙁 😠   Today in a word?   Today's Energy Level

1 2 3 4 5

I'm grateful for...

1. _____

2. _____

3. _____

Today's biggest challenge was...

_____

The best part of today was...

_____

Date: _____

MORNING ☀

Well Okay Badly

I feel... 😊 🙂 😐 🙁 😣   I slept... 🙂 😐 🙁

Today I want to... 💡   ♥ Self Care:

1. _____

2. _____

3. _____

My most important thing today is...

_____

☆ EVENING

I feel... 😊 🙂 😐 🙁 😣

Today in a word?   Today's Energy Level

1 2 3 4 5

I'm grateful for...

1. _____

2. _____

3. _____

Today's biggest challenge was...

_____

The best part of today was...

_____

Date: _____

MORNING ☀

I feel... 😊 🙂 😐 🙁 😣   I slept... Well Okay Badly
                                           🙂 😐 🙁

Today I want to... 💡   ♥ Self Care:

1. _____

2. _____

3. _____

My most important thing today is...

_____

⭐ EVENING

I feel... 😊 🙂 😐 🙁 😣

Today in a word?   Today's Energy Level

I'm grateful for...   1 2 3 4 5

1. _____

2. _____

3. _____

Today's biggest challenge was...

_____

The best part of today was...

_____

Date: _____

MORNING ☀

I feel... 😃 😊 😐 😟 😣   I slept...   Well Okay Badly
                                            😊   😐   😟

Today I want to... 💡   ♡ Self Care:

1. _____

2. _____

3. _____

My most important thing today is...

_____

⭐ EVENING

I feel... 😃 😊 😐 😟 😣

Today in a word?   Today's Energy Level

                                          1 2 3 4 5

I'm grateful for...

1. _____

2. _____

3. _____

Today's biggest challenge was...

_____

The best part of today was...

_____

Date: _____

MORNING ☀

Well Okay Badly

I feel... 😊 🙂 😐 ☹ 😣   I slept... 🙂 😐 ☹

Today I want to... 💡   ♡ Self Care:

1. _____

2. _____

3. _____

My most important thing today is...

_____

☆ EVENING

I feel... 😊 🙂 😐 ☹ 😣   Today in a word?   Today's Energy Level

1 2 3 4 5

I'm grateful for...

1. _____

2. _____

3. _____

Today's biggest challenge was...

_____

The best part of today was...

_____

Date: _____

MORNING ☀

Well Okay Badly

I feel... 😊 🙂 😐 🙁 😣   I slept... 🙂 😐 🙁

Today I want to... 💡   ❤ Self Care:

1. _____

2. _____

3. _____

My most important thing today is...
_____

☆ EVENING

I feel... 😊 🙂 😐 🙁 😣

I'm grateful for...

Today in a word?   Today's Energy Level

1 2 3 4 5

1. _____

2. _____

3. _____

Today's biggest challenge was...
_____

The best part of today was...
_____

Date: _____

MORNING ☀

I feel... 😊 🙂 😐 🙁 😣   I slept... 🙂 😐 🙁

Today I want to... 💡   ♥ Self Care:

1. _____

2. _____

3. _____

My most important thing today is...
_____

⭐ EVENING

I feel... 😊 🙂 😐 🙁 😣   Today in a word?   Today's Energy Level

I'm grateful for...   1 2 3 4 5

1. _____

2. _____

3. _____

Today's biggest challenge was...
_____

The best part of today was...
_____

Date: _____

MORNING ☀

I feel... 😊 🙂 😐 🙁 😣   I slept... 🙂 😐 🙁

Well Okay Badly

Today I want to... 💡   ♥ Self Care:

1. _____

2. _____

3. _____

My most important thing today is...

_____

⭐ EVENING

I feel... 😊 🙂 😐 🙁 😣

Today in a word?   Today's Energy Level

I'm grateful for...   1 2 3 4 5

1. _____

2. _____

3. _____

Today's biggest challenge was...

_____

The best part of today was...

_____

Date: _____

MORNING ☀

Well Okay Badly

I feel... 😊 🙂 😐 🙁 😣   I slept... 🙂 😐 🙁

Today I want to... 💡   ❤ Self Care: _____

1. _____

2. _____

3. _____

My most important thing today is...

_____

⭐ EVENING

I feel... 😊 🙂 😐 🙁 😣   *Today in a word?*   Today's Energy Level

1 2 3 4 5

I'm grateful for...

1. _____

2. _____

3. _____

Today's biggest challenge was...

_____

The best part of today was...

_____

Date: _____

MORNING ☼

I feel... 😊 🙂 😐 🙁 😣   I slept... 🙂 😐 🙁

Well Okay Badly

Today I want to... 💡   ♡ Self Care:

1. _____

2. _____

3. _____

My most important thing today is...
_____

☆ EVENING

I feel... 😊 🙂 😐 🙁 😣

I'm grateful for...

Today in a word?   Today's Energy Level

1 2 3 4 5

1. _____

2. _____

3. _____

Today's biggest challenge was...
_____

The best part of today was...
_____

Date: _____

MORNING ☀

I feel... 😊 🙂 😐 🙁 😣   I slept...   Well Okay Badly
🙂 😐 🙁

Today I want to... 💡   ♥ Self Care:

1. _____

2. _____

3. _____

My most important thing today is...
_____

⭐ EVENING

I feel... 😊 🙂 😐 🙁 😣   Today in a word?   Today's Energy Level

1 2 3 4 5

I'm grateful for...

1. _____

2. _____

3. _____

Today's biggest challenge was...
_____

The best part of today was...
_____

Date: _____

MORNING ☀

I feel... 😊 🙂 😐 🙁 😣   I slept... 🙂 😐 🙁

Well Okay Badly

Today I want to... 💡   ♥ Self Care:

1. _____

2. _____

3. _____

My most important thing today is...
_____

⭐ EVENING

I feel... 😊 🙂 😐 🙁 😣   Today in a word?   Today's Energy Level

1 2 3 4 5

I'm grateful for...

1. _____

2. _____

3. _____

Today's biggest challenge was...
_____

The best part of today was...
_____

Date: _____

MORNING ☼

I feel... 😊 🙂 😐 🙁 😣   I slept... 🙂 😐 🙁
                                        Well Okay Badly

Today I want to... 💡   ♡ Self Care: _____

1. _____

2. _____

3. _____

My most important thing today is...
_____

☆ EVENING

I feel... 😊 🙂 😐 🙁 😣   Today in a word?   Today's Energy Level

I'm grateful for...   1 2 3 4 5

1. _____

2. _____

3. _____

Today's biggest challenge was...
_____

The best part of today was...
_____

Date: _____

MORNING ☀

I feel... 😃 🙂 😐 🙁 😣   I slept...   Well Okay Badly
                                          🙂   😐   🙁

Today I want to... 💡   💗 Self Care:

1. _____

2. _____

3. _____

My most important thing today is...

_____

☆ EVENING

I feel... 😃 🙂 😐 🙁 😣

I'm grateful for...   Today in a word?   Today's Energy Level

                                                        1 2 3 4 5

1. _____

2. _____

3. _____

Today's biggest challenge was...

_____

The best part of today was...

_____

Date: _____

MORNING ☀

I feel... 😊 🙂 😐 😟 😣   I slept...

Well Okay Badly

I slept... 🙂 😐 😟

Today I want to... 💡   ♥ Self Care:

1. _____

2. _____

3. _____

My most important thing today is...
_____

⭐ EVENING

I feel... 😊 🙂 😐 😟 😣

Today in a word?   Today's Energy Level

1 2 3 4 5

I'm grateful for...

1. _____

2. _____

3. _____

Today's biggest challenge was...
_____

The best part of today was...
_____

Date: _____

MORNING ☀

I feel... 😃 🙂 😐 🙁 😣   I slept... 🙂 😐 🙁
                                    Well Okay Badly

Today I want to... 💡   ♥ Self Care:

1. _____

2. _____

3. _____

My most important thing today is...

_____

⭐ EVENING

I feel... 😃 🙂 😐 🙁 😣

I'm grateful for...   Today in a word?   Today's Energy Level
                                                  1 2 3 4 5

1. _____

2. _____

3. _____

Today's biggest challenge was...

_____

The best part of today was...

_____

Date: _____

MORNING ☀

I feel... 😊 🙂 😐 🙁 😣   I slept... Well Okay Badly 🙂 😐 🙁

Today I want to... 💡   ♡ Self Care: _____

1. _____

2. _____

3. _____

My most important thing today is...

_____

⭐ EVENING

I feel... 😊 🙂 😐 🙁 😣   Today in a word?   Today's Energy Level

1 2 3 4 5

I'm grateful for...

1. _____

2. _____

3. _____

Today's biggest challenge was...

_____

The best part of today was...

_____

Date: _____

MORNING ☀

I feel... 😊 🙂 😐 🙁 😣

I slept... Well Okay Badly
🙂 😐 🙁

Today I want to... 💡

♥ Self Care: _____

1. _____

2. _____

3. _____

My most important thing today is...

_____

⭐ EVENING

I feel... 😊 🙂 😐 🙁 😣

Today in a word?

Today's Energy Level

1 2 3 4 5

I'm grateful for...

1. _____

2. _____

3. _____

Today's biggest challenge was...

_____

The best part of today was...

_____

Date: _____

MORNING ☀

I feel... 😋 🙂 😐 🙁 😣   I slept... 🙂 😐 🙁

|Well|Okay|Badly|

Today I want to... 💡   ❤ Self Care:

1. _____

2. _____

3. _____

My most important thing today is...

_____

⭐ EVENING

I feel... 😋 🙂 😐 🙁 😣

Today in a word?   Today's Energy Level

1 2 3 4 5

I'm grateful for...

1. _____

2. _____

3. _____

Today's biggest challenge was...

_____

The best part of today was...

_____

Date: _____

MORNING ☀

I feel... 😊 🙂 😐 🙁 😣   I slept...

I slept... 🙂 😐 🙁

Today I want to... 💡   ♥ Self Care:

1. _____

2. _____

3. _____

My most important thing today is...

_____

⭐ EVENING

I feel... 😊 🙂 😐 🙁 😣

Today in a word?   Today's Energy Level

( )   1 2 3 4 5

I'm grateful for...

1. _____

2. _____

3. _____

Today's biggest challenge was...

_____

The best part of today was...

_____

Date: _____

MORNING ☀

I feel... 😊 🙂 😐 🙁 😣   I slept... Well Okay Badly
                                          🙂   😐   🙁

Today I want to... 💡   ♥ Self Care: _____

1. _____

2. _____

3. _____

My most important thing today is...
_____

⭐ EVENING

I feel... 😊 🙂 😐 🙁 😣   Today in a word?   Today's Energy Level

                          ⬭   1 2 3 4 5

I'm grateful for...

1. _____

2. _____

3. _____

Today's biggest challenge was...
_____

The best part of today was...
_____

Date: _____

MORNING ☀

Well Okay Badly

I feel... 😊 🙂 😐 🙁 😣   I slept... 🙂 😐 🙁

Today I want to... 💡   ♥ Self Care:

1. _____

2. _____

3. _____

My most important thing today is...
_____

☆ EVENING

I feel... 😊 🙂 😐 🙁 😣

Today in a word?

Today's Energy Level

1 2 3 4 5

I'm grateful for...

1. _____

2. _____

3. _____

Today's biggest challenge was...
_____

The best part of today was...
_____

Date: _____

MORNING ☀

Well Okay Badly

I feel... 😋 🙂 😐 🙁 😣   I slept... 🙂 😐 🙁

Today I want to... 💡   ♥ Self Care:

1. _____

2. _____

3. _____

My most important thing today is...

_____

⭐ EVENING

I feel... 😋 🙂 😐 🙁 😣

Today in a word?   Today's Energy Level

1 2 3 4 5

I'm grateful for...

1. _____

2. _____

3. _____

Today's biggest challenge was...

_____

The best part of today was...

_____

Date: _____

MORNING ☀

I feel... 😊 🙂 😐 🙁 😣

I slept...

Well | Okay | Badly

🙂 😐 🙁

Today I want to... 💡

♥ Self Care:

1. _____

2. _____

3. _____

My most important thing today is...

_____

☆ EVENING

I feel... 😊 🙂 😐 🙁 😣

Today in a word?

Today's Energy Level

1 2 3 4 5

I'm grateful for...

1. _____

2. _____

3. _____

Today's biggest challenge was...

_____

The best part of today was...

_____

Date: _____

MORNING ☀

I feel... 😊 🙂 😐 🙁 😣

I slept... Well Okay Badly
😊 😐 🙁

Today I want to... 💡   ♡ Self Care: _____

1. _____

2. _____

3. _____

My most important thing today is...

_____

⭐ EVENING

I feel... 😊 🙂 😐 🙁 😣   Today in a word?   Today's Energy Level

                                                              1 2 3 4 5

I'm grateful for...

1. _____

2. _____

3. _____

Today's biggest challenge was...

_____

The best part of today was...

_____

Date: _____

MORNING ☀

I feel... 😊 🙂 😐 🙁 😣   I slept... Well Okay Badly
                                              🙂   😐   🙁

Today I want to... 💡   💗 Self Care: _____

1. _____

2. _____

3. _____

My most important thing today is...

_____

☆ EVENING

I feel... 😊 🙂 😐 🙁 😣   Today in a word?   Today's Energy Level

                                              (_____)   1 2 3 4 5

I'm grateful for...

1. _____

2. _____

3. _____

Today's biggest challenge was...

_____

The best part of today was...

_____

Date: _____

MORNING ☀

I feel... 😌 😊 😐 ☹ 😣   I slept... 😊 😐 ☹

Today I want to... 💡   ❤ Self Care:

1. _____

2. _____

3. _____

My most important thing today is...

_____

⭐ EVENING

I feel... 😌 😊 😐 ☹ 😣   Today in a word?   Today's Energy Level

1 2 3 4 5

I'm grateful for...

1. _____

2. _____

3. _____

Today's biggest challenge was...

_____

The best part of today was...

_____

Date: _____

MORNING ☼

I feel... 😀 🙂 😐 🙁 😣   I slept...   Well Okay Badly
🙂 😐 🙁

Today I want to... 💡   ❤ Self Care:

1. _____

2. _____

3. _____

My most important thing today is...
_____

☆ EVENING

I feel... 😀 🙂 😐 🙁 😣

Today in a word?   Today's Energy Level

1 2 3 4 5

I'm grateful for...

1. _____

2. _____

3. _____

Today's biggest challenge was...
_____

The best part of today was...
_____

Date: _____

MORNING ☀

Well Okay Badly

I feel... 😀 🙂 😐 🙁 😣   I slept... 🙂 😐 🙁

Today I want to... 💡   ♥ Self Care:

1. _____

2. _____

3. _____

My most important thing today is...

_____

☆ EVENING

I feel... 😀 🙂 😐 🙁 😣

Today in a word?

Today's Energy Level

1 2 3 4 5

I'm grateful for...

1. _____

2. _____

3. _____

Today's biggest challenge was...

_____

The best part of today was...

_____

Date: _____

MORNING ☀

I feel... 😊 🙂 😐 🙁 😖   I slept...   🙂 😐 🙁

Today I want to... 💡   💗 Self Care:

1. _____

2. _____

3. _____

My most important thing today is...

_____

⭐ EVENING

I feel... 😊 🙂 😐 🙁 😖   Today in a word?   Today's Energy Level

1 2 3 4 5

I'm grateful for...

1. _____

2. _____

3. _____

Today's biggest challenge was...

_____

The best part of today was...

_____

Date: _____

MORNING ☀

I feel... 😋 🙂 😐 🙁 😣   I slept... 🙂 😐 🙁
Well Okay Badly

Today I want to... 💡   ♥ Self Care: _____

1. _____

2. _____

3. _____

My most important thing today is...
_____

☆ EVENING

I feel... 😋 🙂 😐 🙁 😣

Today in a word?   Today's Energy Level

1 2 3 4 5

I'm grateful for...

1. _____

2. _____

3. _____

Today's biggest challenge was...
_____

The best part of today was...
_____

Date: _____

MORNING ☀

I feel... 😊 🙂 😐 🙁 😣   I slept... 🙂 😐 🙁

Well Okay Badly

Today I want to... 💡   ♥ Self Care:

1. _____

2. _____

3. _____

My most important thing today is...

_____

☆ EVENING

I feel... 😊 🙂 😐 🙁 😣   Today in a word?   Today's Energy Level

1 2 3 4 5

I'm grateful for...

1. _____

2. _____

3. _____

Today's biggest challenge was...

_____

The best part of today was...

_____

Date: _____

MORNING ☼

I feel... 😊 🙂 😐 🙁 😠   I slept... 🙂 😐 🙁

Well Okay Badly

Today I want to... 💡   ♡ Self Care: _____

1. _____

2. _____

3. _____

My most important thing today is...
_____

⭐ EVENING

I feel... 😊 🙂 😐 🙁 😠

Today in a word?   Today's Energy Level

1 2 3 4 5

I'm grateful for...

1. _____

2. _____

3. _____

Today's biggest challenge was...
_____

The best part of today was...
_____

Date: _____

MORNING ☼

I feel... 😊 🙂 😐 🙁 😠   I slept...
🙂 😐 🙁

Today I want to... 💡   ♥ Self Care:

1. _____

2. _____

3. _____

My most important thing today is...
_____

☆ EVENING

I feel... 😊 🙂 😐 🙁 😠   Today in a word?   Today's Energy Level

                                                        1 2 3 4 5

I'm grateful for...

1. _____

2. _____

3. _____

Today's biggest challenge was...
_____

The best part of today was...
_____

Date: _____

MORNING ☀

I feel... 😋 🙂 😐 🙁 😣   I slept... 🙂 😐 🙁

Today I want to... 💡   ♥ Self Care:

1. _____

2. _____

3. _____

My most important thing today is...

_____

⭐ EVENING

I feel... 😋 🙂 😐 🙁 😣   Today in a word?   Today's Energy Level

          1 2 3 4 5

I'm grateful for...

1. _____

2. _____

3. _____

Today's biggest challenge was...

_____

The best part of today was...

_____

Date: _____

MORNING ☀

I feel... 😋 🙂 😐 🙁 😣

I slept... Well Okay Badly 🙂 😐 🙁

Today I want to... 💡

♥ Self Care:

1. _____

2. _____

3. _____

My most important thing today is...

⭐ EVENING

I feel... 😋 🙂 😐 🙁 😣

Today in a word?

Today's Energy Level
1 2 3 4 5

I'm grateful for...

1. _____

2. _____

3. _____

Today's biggest challenge was...

The best part of today was...

Date: _____

MORNING ☀

I feel... 😊 🙂 😐 🙁 😣   I slept... Well Okay Badly 🙂 😐 🙁

Today I want to... 💡   ♡ Self Care: _____

1. _____

2. _____

3. _____

My most important thing today is...

_____

⭐ EVENING

I feel... 😊 🙂 😐 🙁 😣

Today in a word?

Today's Energy Level

1 2 3 4 5

I'm grateful for...

1. _____

2. _____

3. _____

Today's biggest challenge was...

_____

The best part of today was...

_____

Date: _____

MORNING ☀

Well Okay Badly

I feel... 😊 🙂 😐 🙁 😣   I slept... 🙂 😐 🙁

Today I want to... 💡   ♡ Self Care: _____

1. _____

2. _____

3. _____

My most important thing today is...
_____

★ EVENING

I feel... 😊 🙂 😐 🙁 😣

Today in a word?

Today's Energy Level

1 2 3 4 5

I'm grateful for...

1. _____

2. _____

3. _____

Today's biggest challenge was...
_____

The best part of today was...
_____

Date: _____

MORNING ☀

I feel... 😌 🙂 😐 🙁 😣   I slept... 🙂 😐 🙁

Today I want to... 💡   ❤ Self Care:

1. _____

2. _____

3. _____

My most important thing today is...
_____

⭐ EVENING

I feel... 😌 🙂 😐 🙁 😣   Today in a word?   Today's Energy Level

1 2 3 4 5

I'm grateful for...

1. _____

2. _____

3. _____

Today's biggest challenge was...
_____

The best part of today was...
_____

Date: _____

MORNING ☀

I feel... 😊 🙂 😐 🙁 😣

I slept...

Well Okay Badly

🙂 😐 🙁

Today I want to... 💡

♥ Self Care:

1. _____

2. _____

3. _____

My most important thing today is...

_____

☆ EVENING

I feel... 😊 🙂 😐 🙁 😣

Today in a word?

Today's Energy Level

1 2 3 4 5

I'm grateful for...

1. _____

2. _____

3. _____

Today's biggest challenge was...

_____

The best part of today was...

_____

Date: _____

MORNING ☀

Well   Okay   Badly

I feel... 😋 🙂 😐 🙁 😖   I slept... 🙂 😐 🙁

Today I want to... 💡   ♡ Self Care: _____

1. _____

2. _____

3. _____

My most important thing today is...

_____

⭐ EVENING

I feel... 😋 🙂 😐 🙁 😖   Today in a word?   Today's Energy Level

                                     1 2 3 4 5

I'm grateful for...

1. _____

2. _____

3. _____

Today's biggest challenge was...

_____

The best part of today was...

_____

Date: _____

MORNING ☀

I feel... 😊 🙂 😐 🙁 😣

Well　Okay　Badly

I slept... 🙂 😐 🙁

Today I want to... 💡

♡ Self Care:

1. _____

2. _____

3. _____

My most important thing today is...

_____

☆ EVENING

I feel... 😊 🙂 😐 🙁 😣

Today in a word?

Today's Energy Level

1 2 3 4 5

I'm grateful for...

1. _____

2. _____

3. _____

Today's biggest challenge was...

_____

The best part of today was...

_____

Date: _____

MORNING ☀

I feel... 😋 🙂 😐 🙁 😣   I slept... 🙂 😐 🙁

Well Okay Badly

Today I want to... 💡   ♥ Self Care: _____

1. _____

2. _____

3. _____

My most important thing today is...

_____

⭐ EVENING

I feel... 😋 🙂 😐 🙁 😣

Today in a word?

Today's Energy Level

1 2 3 4 5

I'm grateful for...

1. _____

2. _____

3. _____

Today's biggest challenge was...

_____

The best part of today was...

_____

Date: _____

MORNING ☀

I feel... 😌 🙂 😐 🙁 😣   I slept...   Well   Okay   Badly
                                          🙂   😐   🙁

Today I want to... 💡   💛 Self Care: _____

1. _____

2. _____

3. _____

My most important thing today is...
_____

⭐ EVENING

I feel... 😠 🙂 😐 🙁 😣   Today in a word?   Today's Energy Level

I'm grateful for...   1 2 3 4 5

1. _____

2. _____

3. _____

Today's biggest challenge was...
_____

The best part of today was...
_____

Date: _____

MORNING ☀

Well Okay Badly

I feel... 😊 🙂 😐 🙁 😠   I slept... 🙂 😐 🙁

Today I want to... 💡   ♡ Self Care:

1. _____

2. _____

3. _____

My most important thing today is...

_____

⭐ EVENING

I feel... 😊 🙂 😐 🙁 😠

Today in a word?   Today's Energy Level

I'm grateful for...   **1 2 3 4 5**

1. _____

2. _____

3. _____

Today's biggest challenge was...

_____

The best part of today was...

_____

Date: _____

MORNING ☼

I feel... 😊 🙂 😐 🙁 😠   I slept... 🙂 😐 🙁

Well   Okay   Badly

Today I want to... 💡   ♡ Self Care:

1. _____

2. _____

3. _____

My most important thing today is...

_____

☆ EVENING

I feel... 😊 🙂 😐 🙁 😠

Today in a word?   Today's Energy Level

1 2 3 4 5

I'm grateful for...

1. _____

2. _____

3. _____

Today's biggest challenge was...

_____

The best part of today was...

_____

Date: _____

MORNING ☀

I feel... 😊 🙂 😐 🙁 😣   I slept... 🙂 😐 🙁

Well Okay Badly

Today I want to... 💡   ❤ Self Care:

1. _____

2. _____

3. _____

My most important thing today is...
_____

⭐ EVENING

I feel... 😊 🙂 😐 🙁 😣

Today in a word?

Today's Energy Level

1 2 3 4 5

I'm grateful for...

1. _____

2. _____

3. _____

Today's biggest challenge was...
_____

The best part of today was...
_____

Date: _____

MORNING ☀

I feel... 😊 🙂 😐 🙁 😣   I slept... 🙂 😐 🙁

Well   Okay   Badly

Today I want to... 💡   ♡ Self Care: _____

1. _____

2. _____

3. _____

My most important thing today is...

_____

☆ EVENING

I feel... 😊 🙂 😐 🙁 😣

Today in a word?
(   )

Today's Energy Level
1 2 3 4 5

I'm grateful for...

1. _____

2. _____

3. _____

Today's biggest challenge was...

_____

The best part of today was...

_____

Date: _____

MORNING ☀

I feel... 😊 🙂 😐 🙁 😠   I slept... Well Okay Badly 🙂 😐 🙁

Today I want to... 💡   ♥ Self Care: _____

1. _____

2. _____

3. _____

My most important thing today is...

_____

⭐ EVENING

I feel... 😊 🙂 😐 🙁 😠   Today in a word?   Today's Energy Level

⬭   1 2 3 4 5

I'm grateful for...

1. _____

2. _____

3. _____

Today's biggest challenge was...

_____

The best part of today was...

_____

Date: _____

MORNING ☀

I feel... 😊 🙂 😐 🙁 😣

Well Okay Badly

I slept... 🙂 😐 🙁

Today I want to... 💡

♥ Self Care: _____

1. _____

2. _____

3. _____

My most important thing today is...

_____

⭐ EVENING

I feel... 😊 🙂 😐 🙁 😣

Today in a word?

Today's Energy Level

1 2 3 4 5

I'm grateful for...

1. _____

2. _____

3. _____

Today's biggest challenge was...

_____

The best part of today was...

_____

Date: _____

MORNING ☀

I feel... 😛 🙂 😐 🙁 😣   I slept... Well Okay Badly 🙂 😐 🙁

Today I want to... 💡   ❤ Self Care:

1. _____

2. _____

3. _____

My most important thing today is...

_____

⭐ EVENING

I feel... 😛 🙂 😐 🙁 😣   Today in a word?   Today's Energy Level

1 2 3 4 5

I'm grateful for...

1. _____

2. _____

3. _____

Today's biggest challenge was...

_____

The best part of today was...

_____

Date: _____

MORNING ☼

I feel... 😌 🙂 😐 🙁 😣

I slept... Well Okay Badly 🙂 😐 🙁

Today I want to... 💡

♡ Self Care:

1. _____

2. _____

3. _____

My most important thing today is...
_____

☆ EVENING

I feel... 😌 🙂 😐 🙁 😣

I'm grateful for...

Today in a word?

Today's Energy Level

1 2 3 4 5

1. _____

2. _____

3. _____

Today's biggest challenge was...
_____

The best part of today was...
_____

Date: _____

MORNING ☼

Well Okay Badly

I feel... 😊 🙂 😐 🙁 😣   I slept... 🙂 😐 🙁

Today I want to... 💡   ♡ Self Care:

1. _____

2. _____

3. _____

My most important thing today is...
_____

☆ EVENING

I feel... 😊 🙂 😐 🙁 😣   Today in a word?   Today's Energy Level

1 2 3 4 5

I'm grateful for...

1. _____

2. _____

3. _____

Today's biggest challenge was...
_____

The best part of today was...
_____

Date: _____

MORNING ☀

I feel... 😀 🙂 😐 🙁 😣   I slept...   Well Okay Badly
🙂 😐 🙁

Today I want to... 💡   ♥ Self Care:

1. _____

2. _____

3. _____

My most important thing today is...
_____

☆ EVENING

I feel... 😀 🙂 😐 🙁 😣   Today in a word?   Today's Energy Level

I'm grateful for...   1 2 3 4 5

1. _____

2. _____

3. _____

Today's biggest challenge was...
_____

The best part of today was...
_____

Date: _____

MORNING

I feel... 😋 🙂 😐 🙁 😣   I slept... Well Okay Badly 🙂 😐 🙁

Today I want to... 💡   ♥ Self Care:

1. _____

2. _____

3. _____

My most important thing today is...

_____

⭐ EVENING

I feel... 😋 🙂 😐 🙁 😣   Today in a word?   Today's Energy Level 1 2 3 4 5

I'm grateful for...

1. _____

2. _____

3. _____

Today's biggest challenge was...

_____

The best part of today was...

_____

Date: _____

MORNING ☀

I feel... 😊 🙂 😐 🙁 😣   I slept... 🙂 😐 🙁

Today I want to... 💡   ♡ Self Care: _____

1. _____

2. _____

3. _____

My most important thing today is...

_____

⭐ EVENING

I feel... 😊 🙂 😐 🙁 😣

Today in a word?

Today's Energy Level

1 2 3 4 5

I'm grateful for...

1. _____

2. _____

3. _____

Today's biggest challenge was...

_____

The best part of today was...

_____

Date: _____

MORNING ☼

I feel... 😊 🙂 😐 😕 😣   I slept... Well Okay Badly 🙂 😐 😕

Today I want to... 💡   ♥ Self Care: _____

1. _____

2. _____

3. _____

My most important thing today is...
_____

☆ EVENING

I feel... 😊 🙂 😐 😕 😣   Today in a word?   Today's Energy Level

I'm grateful for...   1 2 3 4 5

1. _____

2. _____

3. _____

Today's biggest challenge was...
_____

The best part of today was...
_____

Date: _____

MORNING ☼

I feel... 😊 🙂 😐 🙁 😣   I slept... Well Okay Badly

Today I want to... 💡   ♥ Self Care:

1. _____

2. _____

3. _____

My most important thing today is...

_____

☆ EVENING

I feel... 😊 🙂 😐 🙁 😣   Today in a word?   Today's Energy Level

1 2 3 4 5

I'm grateful for...

1. _____

2. _____

3. _____

Today's biggest challenge was...

_____

The best part of today was...

_____

Date: _____

MORNING ☀

Well Okay Badly

I feel... 😌 🙂 😐 🙁 😣   I slept... 🙂 😐 🙁

Today I want to... 💡   ❤ Self Care: _____

1. _____

2. _____

3. _____

My most important thing today is...

_____

☆ EVENING

I feel... 😌 🙂 😐 🙁 😣   Today in a word?   Today's Energy Level

I'm grateful for...   1 2 3 4 5

1. _____

2. _____

3. _____

Today's biggest challenge was...

_____

The best part of today was...

_____

Date: _____

MORNING ☀

I feel... 😋 🙂 😐 🙁 😣   I slept... Well Okay Badly
                                          🙂   😐   🙁

Today I want to... 💡   ♥ Self Care:

1. _____

2. _____

3. _____

My most important thing today is...

_____

☆ EVENING

I feel... 😋 🙂 😐 🙁 😣

I'm grateful for...

Today in a word?   Today's Energy Level

                          1 2 3 4 5

1. _____

2. _____

3. _____

Today's biggest challenge was...

_____

The best part of today was...

_____

Date: _____

MORNING ☀

I feel... 😊 🙂 😐 🙁 😣   I slept... 🙂 😐 🙁

Today I want to... 💡   ♥ Self Care:

1. _____

2. _____

3. _____

My most important thing today is...
_____

⭐ EVENING

I feel... 😊 🙂 😐 🙁 😣   Today in a word?   Today's Energy Level

I'm grateful for...   1 2 3 4 5

1. _____

2. _____

3. _____

Today's biggest challenge was...
_____

The best part of today was...
_____

Date: _____

MORNING ☀

I feel... 😊 🙂 😐 🙁 😣   I slept...   Well Okay Badly
                                                       🙂   😐   🙁

Today I want to... 💡   ♥ Self Care: _____

1. _____

2. _____

3. _____

My most important thing today is...

_____

⭐ EVENING

I feel... 😊 🙂 😐 🙁 😣   Today in a word?   Today's Energy Level

I'm grateful for...   1 2 3 4 5

1. _____

2. _____

3. _____

Today's biggest challenge was...

_____

The best part of today was...

_____

Date: _____

MORNING ☼

I feel... 😊 🙂 😐 🙁 😣   I slept... 🙂 😐 🙁

Today I want to... 💡   ❤️ Self Care:

1. _____

2. _____

3. _____

My most important thing today is...

_____

⭐ EVENING

I feel... 😊 🙂 😐 🙁 😣   Today in a word?   Today's Energy Level

1 2 3 4 5

I'm grateful for...

1. _____

2. _____

3. _____

Today's biggest challenge was...

_____

The best part of today was...

_____

Date: _____

MORNING ☀

I feel... 😃 🙂 😐 🙁 😣   I slept... (Well) (Okay) (Badly)

Today I want to... 💡   ♡ Self Care: _____

1. _____

2. _____

3. _____

My most important thing today is...

_____

☆ EVENING

I feel... 😃 🙂 😐 🙁 😣

Today in a word? 💬   Today's Energy Level: 1 2 3 4 5

I'm grateful for...

1. _____

2. _____

3. _____

Today's biggest challenge was...

_____

The best part of today was...

_____

Date: _____

MORNING ☀

I feel... 😊 🙂 😐 🙁 😣   I slept...   Well Okay Badly
🙂 😐 🙁

Today I want to... 💡   ♡ Self Care: _____

1. _____

2. _____

3. _____

My most important thing today is...
_____

⭐ EVENING

I feel... 😊 🙂 😐 🙁 😣   Today in a word?   Today's Energy Level

I'm grateful for...   (_____)   1 2 3 4 5

1. _____

2. _____

3. _____

Today's biggest challenge was...
_____

The best part of today was...
_____

Date: _____

MORNING ☼

I feel... 😊 🙂 😐 🙁 😣   I slept... Well Okay Badly
🙂 😐 🙁

Today I want to... 💡   ♥ Self Care:

1. _____

2. _____

3. _____

My most important thing today is...
_____

☆ EVENING

I feel... 😊 🙂 😐 🙁 😣   Today in a word?   Today's Energy Level

I'm grateful for...   1 2 3 4 5

1. _____

2. _____

3. _____

Today's biggest challenge was...
_____

The best part of today was...
_____

Date: _____

MORNING ☀

I feel... 😋 🙂 😐 🙁 😣   I slept...   _{Well} _{Okay} _{Badly} 🙂 😐 🙁

Today I want to... 💡   ♡ Self Care: _____

1. _____

2. _____

3. _____

My most important thing today is...

_____

⭐ EVENING

I feel... 😋 🙂 😐 🙁 😣

I'm grateful for...

Today in a word?   Today's Energy Level

                          1 2 3 4 5

1. _____

2. _____

3. _____

Today's biggest challenge was...

_____

The best part of today was...

_____

Date: _____

MORNING ☀

I feel... 😊 🙂 😐 🙁 😣   I slept...   Well Okay Badly
                                              🙂   😐   🙁

Today I want to... 💡   ♡ Self Care:

1. _____

2. _____

3. _____

My most important thing today is...

_____

☆ EVENING

I feel... 😊 🙂 😐 🙁 😣   Today in a word?   Today's Energy Level

I'm grateful for...   1 2 3 4 5

1. _____

2. _____

3. _____

Today's biggest challenge was...

_____

The best part of today was...

_____

Date: _____

MORNING ☀

I feel... 😊 🙂 😐 🙁 😠   I slept... Well Okay Badly 🙂 😐 🙁

Today I want to... 💡   ♡ Self Care: _____

1. _____

2. _____

3. _____

My most important thing today is...
_____

⭐ EVENING

I feel... 😊 🙂 😐 🙁 😠   Today in a word?   Today's Energy Level

I'm grateful for...   1 2 3 4 5

1. _____

2. _____

3. _____

Today's biggest challenge was...
_____

The best part of today was...
_____

Date: _____

MORNING ☀

I feel... 😊 🙂 😐 🙁 😣   I slept...

Well   Okay   Badly
🙂   😐   🙁

Today I want to... 💡   ♥ Self Care:

1. _____

2. _____

3. _____

My most important thing today is...

_____

☆ EVENING

I feel... 😊 🙂 😐 🙁 😣

Today in a word?

Today's Energy Level

1 2 3 4 5

I'm grateful for...

1. _____

2. _____

3. _____

Today's biggest challenge was...

_____

The best part of today was...

_____

Date: _____

MORNING ☀

Well Okay Badly

I feel... 😌 🙂 😐 🙁 😣   I slept... 🙂 😐 🙁

Today I want to... 💡   ♥ Self Care:

1. _____

2. _____

3. _____

My most important thing today is...
_____

☆ EVENING

I feel... 😌 🙂 😐 🙁 😣

Today in a word?

Today's Energy Level

1 2 3 4 5

I'm grateful for...

1. _____

2. _____

3. _____

Today's biggest challenge was...
_____

The best part of today was...
_____

Date: _____

MORNING ☀

Well Okay Badly

I feel... 😊 🙂 😐 ☹ 😣   I slept... 🙂 😐 ☹

Today I want to... 💡   ♥ Self Care:

1. _____

2. _____

3. _____

My most important thing today is...
_____

⭐ EVENING

I feel... 😊 🙂 😐 ☹ 😣

Today in a word?   Today's Energy Level

1 2 3 4 5

I'm grateful for...

1. _____

2. _____

3. _____

Today's biggest challenge was...
_____

The best part of today was...
_____

Date: _____

MORNING ☀

Well Okay Badly

I feel... 😊 🙂 😐 🙁 😣   I slept... 🙂 😐 🙁

Today I want to... 💡   ♥ Self Care: _____

1. _____

2. _____

3. _____

My most important thing today is...
_____

⭐ EVENING

I feel... 😊 🙂 😐 🙁 😣   Today in a word?   Today's Energy Level

1 2 3 4 5

I'm grateful for...

1. _____

2. _____

3. _____

Today's biggest challenge was...
_____

The best part of today was...
_____

Date: _____

MORNING ☀

I feel... 😊 🙂 😐 🙁 😣   I slept... Well Okay Badly
                                            🙂   😐   🙁

Today I want to... 💡   ♡ Self Care:

1. _____

2. _____

3. _____

My most important thing today is...

_____

⭐ EVENING

I feel... 😊 🙂 😐 🙁 😣

Today in a word?

Today's Energy Level

1 2 3 4 5

I'm grateful for...

1. _____

2. _____

3. _____

Today's biggest challenge was...

_____

The best part of today was...

_____

Date: _____

MORNING ☀

I feel... 😌 🙂 😐 ☹ 😣   I slept... Well Okay Badly 🙂 😐 ☹

Today I want to... 💡   ♥ Self Care:

1. _____

2. _____

3. _____

My most important thing today is...

_____

☆ EVENING

I feel... 😌 🙂 😐 ☹ 😣   Today in a word?   Today's Energy Level

1 2 3 4 5

I'm grateful for...

1. _____

2. _____

3. _____

Today's biggest challenge was...

_____

The best part of today was...

_____

Date: _____

MORNING ☀

I feel... 😊 🙂 😐 😕 😣   I slept... Well Okay Badly
                                          🙂   😐   😟

Today I want to... 💡   ♡ Self Care:

1. _____

2. _____

3. _____

My most important thing today is...
_____

☆ EVENING

I feel... 😊 🙂 😐 😕 😣   Today in a word?   Today's Energy Level

                                                           1 2 3 4 5

I'm grateful for...

1. _____

2. _____

3. _____

Today's biggest challenge was...
_____

The best part of today was...
_____

Date: _____

MORNING ☼

I feel... 😊 🙂 😐 🙁 😠   I slept... Well Okay Badly 😊 😐 🙁

Today I want to... 💡   ♥ Self Care: _____

1. _____

2. _____

3. _____

My most important thing today is... _____

⭐ EVENING

I feel... 😊 🙂 😐 🙁 😠   Today in a word?   Today's Energy Level

1 2 3 4 5

I'm grateful for...

1. _____

2. _____

3. _____

Today's biggest challenge was... _____

The best part of today was... _____

Date: _____

MORNING ☀

I feel... 😊 🙂 😐 🙁 😣

I slept... Well Okay Badly
            🙂   😐   🙁

Today I want to... 💡

♥ Self Care: _____

1. _____

2. _____

3. _____

My most important thing today is...

_____

☆ EVENING

I feel... 😊 🙂 😐 🙁 😣

Today in a word?

Today's Energy Level

1 2 3 4 5

I'm grateful for...

1. _____

2. _____

3. _____

Today's biggest challenge was...

_____

The best part of today was...

_____

Date: _____

MORNING

I feel... 😐 🙂 😐 🙁 😣   I slept...

Well Okay Badly

🙂 😐 🙁

Today I want to... 💡   ❤️ Self Care:

1. _____

2. _____

3. _____

My most important thing today is...

_____

⭐ EVENING

I feel... 😐 🙂 😐 🙁 😣

Today in a word?

Today's Energy Level

1 2 3 4 5

I'm grateful for...

1. _____

2. _____

3. _____

Today's biggest challenge was...

_____

The best part of today was...

_____

Date: _____

MORNING ☀

I feel... 😗 🙂 😐 🙁 😣   I slept... Well Okay Badly
                                         🙂   😐   🙁

Today I want to... 💡   ♥ Self Care:

1. _____

2. _____

3. _____

My most important thing today is...

_____

⭐ EVENING

I feel... 😗 🙂 😐 🙁 😣

I'm grateful for...

Today in a word?   Today's Energy Level

                          1 2 3 4 5

1. _____

2. _____

3. _____

Today's biggest challenge was...

_____

The best part of today was...

_____

Date: _____

MORNING ☀

Well Okay Badly

I feel... 😊 🙂 😐 🙁 😣   I slept... 🙂 😐 🙁

Today I want to... 💡   ♡ Self Care:

1. _____

2. _____

3. _____

My most important thing today is...
_____

☆ EVENING

I feel... 😊 🙂 😐 🙁 😣   Today in a word?   Today's Energy Level

I'm grateful for...   1 2 3 4 5

1. _____

2. _____

3. _____

Today's biggest challenge was...
_____

The best part of today was...
_____

Date: _____

MORNING ☀

I feel... 😊 🙂 😐 🙁 😣   I slept...   Well Okay Badly

😊 😐 🙁

Today I want to... 💡   ♥ Self Care:

1. _____

2. _____

3. _____

My most important thing today is...

_____

☆ EVENING

I feel... 😊 🙂 😐 🙁 😣   Today in a word?   Today's Energy Level

1 2 3 4 5

I'm grateful for...

1. _____

2. _____

3. _____

Today's biggest challenge was...

_____

The best part of today was...

_____

Date: _____

MORNING ☀

I feel... 😋 🙂 😐 🙁 😣   I slept... 🙂 😐 🙁
                                           Well Okay Badly

Today I want to... 💡   ♥ Self Care: _____

1. _____

2. _____

3. _____

My most important thing today is...

_____

⭐ EVENING

I feel... 😋 🙂 😐 🙁 😣   Today in a word?   Today's Energy Level

I'm grateful for...   1 2 3 4 5

1. _____

2. _____

3. _____

Today's biggest challenge was...

_____

The best part of today was...

_____

Date: _____

MORNING ☀

I feel... 😃 🙂 😐 🙁 😖   I slept... 🙂 😐 🙁

Today I want to... 💡   ♥ Self Care:

1. _____

2. _____

3. _____

My most important thing today is...

_____

⭐ EVENING

I feel... 😃 🙂 😐 🙁 😖   Today in a word?   Today's Energy Level

1 2 3 4 5

I'm grateful for...

1. _____

2. _____

3. _____

Today's biggest challenge was...

_____

The best part of today was...

_____

Date: _____

MORNING ☀

I feel... 😊 🙂 😐 🙁 😣   I slept... Well Okay Badly
🙂 😐 🙁

Today I want to... 💡   ♡ Self Care: _____

1. _____

2. _____

3. _____

My most important thing today is...

_____

⭐ EVENING

I feel... 😊 🙂 😐 🙁 😣   Today in a word?   Today's Energy Level

I'm grateful for...   (_____)   1 2 3 4 5

1. _____

2. _____

3. _____

Today's biggest challenge was...

_____

The best part of today was...

_____

Date: _____

MORNING ☀

I feel... 😊 🙂 😐 🙁 😣   I slept... 🙂 😐 🙁
                                    Well Okay Badly

Today I want to... 💡   ♥ Self Care:

1. _____

2. _____

3. _____

My most important thing today is...

_____

☆ EVENING

I feel... 😊 🙂 😐 🙁 😣

Today in a word?   Today's Energy Level

                        1 2 3 4 5

I'm grateful for...

1. _____

2. _____

3. _____

Today's biggest challenge was...

_____

The best part of today was...

_____

Date: _____

MORNING ☀

I feel... 😊 🙂 😐 🙁 😣   I slept... 🙂 😐 🙁

Well Okay Badly

Today I want to... 💡   ♥ Self Care:

1. _____

2. _____

3. _____

My most important thing today is...
_____

⭐ EVENING

I feel... 😊 🙂 😐 🙁 😣

Today in a word?   Today's Energy Level

1 2 3 4 5

I'm grateful for...

1. _____

2. _____

3. _____

Today's biggest challenge was...
_____

The best part of today was...
_____